A
VIEW
OF THE
UNIVERSE

A Book of Postcards

Pomegranate Artbooks / San Francisco

Pomegranate Artbooks
Box 6099
Rohnert Park, CA 94927

ISBN 0-87654-101-5
Pomegranate Catalog No. A758

Photographs by David Malin, Anglo-Australian Observatory
© 1994 Anglo-Australian Telescope Board
© 1994 ROE/AAT Board

Many of the images in this book of postcards are from
the book *A View of the Universe*, by David Malin
(Sky Publishing Corporation and Cambridge University Press, 1993).

Pomegranate publishes books of
postcards on a wide range of subjects.
Please write to the publisher for more information.

Designed by Mark Koenig
Printed in Korea

THE ANGLO-AUSTRALIAN OBSERVATORY

is jointly and equally funded by the British and Australian governments. It operates the 3.9 m (150 in.) Anglo-Australian telescope (AAT) and the 1.2 m (48 in.) United Kingdom Schmidt telescope (UKST). Both telescopes are located at Siding Springs Observatory in northwestern New South Wales, far away from city lights. The instruments are at the forefront of modern astronomical research and together have discovered an astonishing range of astronomical objects, among them some of the most distant and faintest ever detected.

The images in this book of postcards were made by David Malin from plates taken on both of the Anglo-Australian Observatory's telescopes. They were produced by combining images photographed separately in red, green and blue light, a complex process made necessary because color films are not sensitive enough to record very faint objects. Many of the images shown here are new and show features that have never before been seen in color. Despite their uniqueness, these pictures are an accurate reflection of the colors of the universe, much as the eye might see them if it could be made a million times more sensitive.

A VIEW OF THE UNIVERSE

BETWEEN THE ORION AND HORSEHEAD NEBULAE

This wide angle view of part of Orion shows the distinctive Horsehead and much brighter Orion nebulae, both about 1,500 light years distant. In this region radio astronomers have found extensive molecular clouds normally invisible at optical wavelengths. However, between these two nebula there is just enough light to feebly illuminate these dark regions, producing the wispy tendrils in the middle of the picture.

Pomegranate, Box 6099, Rohnert Park, CA 94927

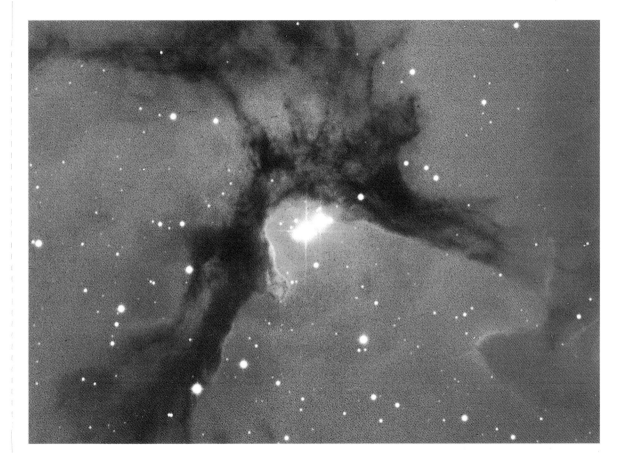

A VIEW OF THE UNIVERSE

THE STARS AT THE HEART OF M20

M20, the Trifid Nebula, surrounds a star-forming region in the southern constellation of Sagittarius. Where the dust lanes intersect is a compact group of stars that provide the energy to excite a cloud of hydrogen forty light years across. The bright rims outlining the dark lanes show that the stars and dust are intimately associated.

Pomegranate, Box 6099, Rohnert Park, CA 94927

A VIEW OF THE UNIVERSE

MESSIER 84 AND 86 IN THE VIRGO CLUSTER OF GALAXIES
The cloud of galaxies in Virgo, about 50 million light years away, is the nearest moderately rich galaxy cluster. The densest region centers on the enormous elliptical galaxies M84 and M86, which dominate this photograph. The most numerous members of the cluster are dwarf ellipticals, a few of which can be seen as faint, fuzzy blobs just visible above the sky background.

Pomegranate, Box 6099, Rohnert Park, CA 94927

A VIEW OF THE UNIVERSE

THE TOBY JUG NEBULA
The Toby Jug Nebula, IC 2220, is so named because its shape
resembles that of an English drinking vessel. The nebula
surrounds a bright but cool star and is the result of light
reflected from particles that the star itself has ejected.

Pomegranate, Box 6099, Rohnert Park, CA 94927

A VIEW OF THE UNIVERSE

THE CORONA AUSTRALIS REFLECTION NEBULA

Five hundred light years away in the Corona Australis region, a group of stars lights up a small part of a huge dust cloud, producing the beautiful blue reflection nebulae NGC 6726–27. Also visible are at least two small, well-defined red nebulae that glow by absorbing energy from the stars and re-emitting it in characteristic colors.

Pomegranate, Box 6099, Rohnert Park, CA 94927

A VIEW OF THE UNIVERSE

THE HELIX NEBULA, NGC 7293

NGC 7293, the Helix Nebula, is the nearest of the planetary nebulae and so appears to be the largest. At more than half a degree across, it is about the same apparent size as the full moon. The nebula is excited by a white dwarf star at its center, the exposed core of the star that produced it.

Pomegranate, Box 6099, Rohnert Park, CA 94927

A VIEW OF THE UNIVERSE

THE CONE NEBULA

In this photograph the "cone" is similar to the Horsehead
Nebula, a dusty protuberance illuminated by a bright star.
Also here are a few distinctive yellow nebulae, light from
young stars hidden in the bright cloud, scattered as it
percolates through the dust. These features are often
associated with star formation.

Pomegranate, Box 6099, Rohnert Park, CA 94927

A VIEW OF THE UNIVERSE

FINE STRUCTURES IN THE VELA SUPERNOVA REMNANT

A supernova explosion marks the sudden end to the life of a massive star. As the shock wave encounters traces of tenuous gas between the stars, it creates a faint but highly convoluted nebula, the crinkled surface tinted red and blue. The green line is the trail of an earth-orbiting satellite.

Pomegranate, Box 6099, Rohnert Park, CA 94927

A VIEW OF THE UNIVERSE

HALLEY'S COMET ON DECEMBER 9, 1985

As the Anglo-Australian Telescope followed the rapid movement of Halley's Comet through the solar system, background stars were recorded as streaks, their lengths corresponding to exposure times of 20, 15 and 20 minutes in red, green and blue light. The coma is tinged blue by sunlight acting on gases from the comet's icy nucleus.

Pomegranate, Box 6099, Rohnert Park, CA 94927

A VIEW OF THE UNIVERSE

THE HORSEHEAD NEBULA AND NGC 2024 IN ORION
Energetic radiation from Sigma Orionis, the naked-eye star at
the top of the picture, illuminates the surface of an otherwise
invisible dusty cloud, exciting the distinctive red emission from
hydrogen. From this dark cloud projects yet more dust, which
has the shape of the head of a horse, seen in silhouette against
the glowing background.

Pomegranate, Box 6099, Rohnert Park, CA 94927

A VIEW OF THE UNIVERSE

A BARRED SPIRAL GALAXY IN FORNAX, NGC 1365
Among the most eye-catching of all galaxies are the spirals,
especially barred spirals, of which NGC 1365 is a fine example.
This beautiful galaxy is about as massive as the Milky Way, and
it is the largest spiral in a cluster of galaxies in the southern
constellation of Fornax.

Pomegranate, Box 6099, Rohnert Park, CA 94927

A VIEW OF THE UNIVERSE

THE REFLECTION NEBULA IN THE PLEIADES STAR CLUSTER
The nebula surrounding the Pleiades, or Seven Sisters, is
caused by starlight reflected from tiny particles in a cloud of
cold gas and dust into which the star cluster has drifted. The
nebula's streaky appearance results from alignment of the
particles by magnetic fields between the stars.

Pomegranate, Box 6099, Rohnert Park, CA 94927

A VIEW OF THE UNIVERSE

PART OF THE SUPERNOVA REMNANT IN VELA
About 120 centuries ago an inconspicuous star in the
constellation of Vela suddenly brightened by about a million
times to rival the moon as the brightest object in the night sky.
This photograph shows a part of a huge, expanding nebulous
shell, which now surrounds the site of the explosion.

Pomegranate, Box 6099, Rohnert Park, CA 94927

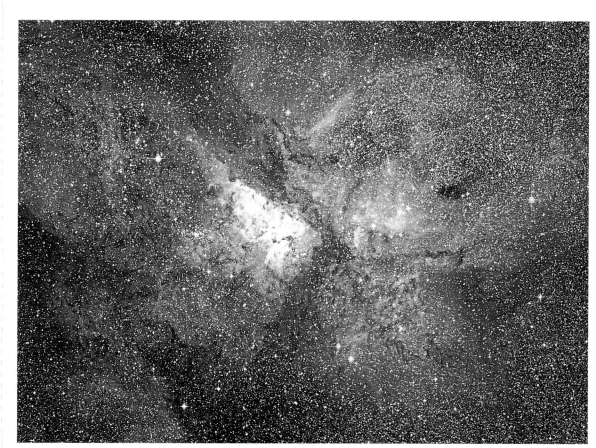

A VIEW OF THE UNIVERSE

THE GREAT NEBULA IN CARINA, NGC 3372
This enormous cloud of glowing hydrogen in the southern
Milky Way is one of the largest and most spectacular star-
forming regions in the galaxy. The combined radiation of its
wealth of hot stars produces the spectacular nebula that
dominates this picture.

Pomegranate, Box 6099, Rohnert Park, CA 94927

A VIEW OF THE UNIVERSE

THE LOOPED EMISSION NEBULA, NGC 3576
This large complex of gas and dust is in the southern
constellation of Carina and is about 7,000 light years away. The
huge octopus-like loops of glowing gas are created by hot
stars hidden in the dusty cloud at the base of the nebula.

Pomegranate, Box 6099, Rohnert Park, CA 94927

A VIEW OF THE UNIVERSE

THE CLUSTER OF GALAXIES IN FORNAX

Galaxies fall into two broad groups, spirals and ellipticals. A spiral galaxy, NGC 1365, is seen in one corner of this group of galaxies in Fornax, 55 million light years away. Most of the others shown here are elliptical galaxies, which can have a shape anywhere between a perfect sphere and an American football and are composed of billions of old, yellowish stars.

Pomegranate, Box 6099, Rohnert Park, CA 94927

A VIEW OF THE UNIVERSE

REFLECTION NEBULA IN ORION, NGC 1973–75–77
This sparkling group of stars embedded in dust and gas is just
half a degree north of the famous and much brighter Orion
Nebula. The cluster can be seen with the unaided eye as a
single object, the northernmost star in the Sword of Orion, and
is about 1,500 light years distant.

Pomegranate, Box 6099, Rohnert Park, CA 94927

A VIEW OF THE UNIVERSE

NEBULOSITY IN SAGITTARIUS, NGC 6589 AND NGC 6590
Huge clouds of interstellar dust give the Milky Way a distinctive
patchy appearance. Here, in the direction of the constellation
Sagittarius, bright stars within the densest dust produce two
bright blue reflection nebulae, NGC 6589 and NGC 6590;
where the dust is thinner, a hydrogen cloud glows with a
characteristic magenta hue.

Pomegranate, Box 6099, Rohnert Park, CA 94927

A VIEW OF THE UNIVERSE

ANTARES AND REFLECTION NEBULA AROUND RHO OPHIUCHUS

On the border between the southern constellations of Ophiuchus and Scorpius are some of the faintest yet most spectacular nebulae ever photographed. The different shades of color are probably an indication of the nature of the dust that the stars create and that swirls between them.

Pomegranate, Box 6099, Rohnert Park, CA 94927

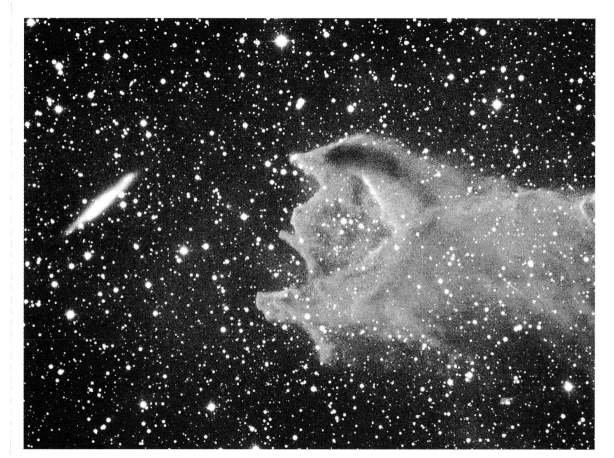

A VIEW OF THE UNIVERSE

THE HEAD OF CG 4, A FAINT COMETARY GLOBULE
Cometary globules are isolated, relatively small clouds of gas and dust within the Milky Way. Energy from adjacent stars gradually sweeps particles from a cometary globule's head, creating its characteristic long tail. This globule seems about to devour an edge-on spiral galaxy, which in reality is millions of light years beyond.

Pomegranate, Box 6099, Rohnert Park, CA 94927

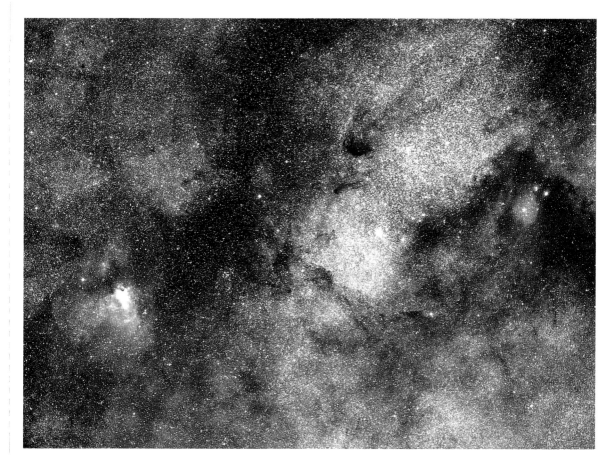

A VIEW OF THE UNIVERSE

MILKY WAY STAR CLOUDS AND MESSIER 17
French astronomer Charles Messier (1730–1817) listed over
100 non-stellar astronomical objects, three of which appear in
this picture. Just to the left of the bright red star-forming
region M17 is M18, a group of stars in a dark region of the
Milky Way. The rich cloud of stars in the middle of the
photograph is M24.

Pomegranate, Box 6099, Rohnert Park, CA 94927

A VIEW OF THE UNIVERSE

AN UNCATALOGUED DARK CLOUD IN SCORPIUS

This curious nebula, reminiscent of the Horsehead Nebula in
Orion, is a cloud of dusty gas illuminated by the Scorpius OB
association, a group of brilliant, hot stars about 5,000 light
years away (outside the picture, to the lower left). Such dark
clouds are common between the stars of the Milky Way, but
few are illuminated in this way.

Pomegranate, Box 6099, Rohnert Park, CA 94927

A VIEW OF THE UNIVERSE

THE DUST LANES AND STAR CLUSTERS IN MESSIER 16
Messier 16 is a mass of glowing gas surrounding a group of young stars in the southern Milky Way. The nebula is a cloud of luminous hydrogen, crisscrossed by dark fingers of dust. The cluster of stars formed from this unlikely mixture about two million years ago, and it provides the energy that causes the nebula to glow.

Pomegranate, Box 6099, Rohnert Park, CA 94927

A VIEW OF THE UNIVERSE

THE GLOBULAR CLUSTER 47 TUCANAE (NGC 104)
Globular clusters are ancient cities of stars formed billions of years before the sun appeared. Though their light is dominated by "red giant" stars, in reality they are no redder than a tungsten lamp; thus 47 Tuc's true color is close to the pale yellow reproduced here. The core of 47 Tuc is so crowded that stars sometimes interact, forming pulsars.

Pomegranate, Box 6099, Rohnert Park, CA 94927

A VIEW OF THE UNIVERSE

THE GREAT NEBULA IN THE SWORD-HANDLE OF ORION
The Orion Nebula, the nearest star-forming region, is 1,500 light years away, and it is its proximity rather than its size that is responsible for its spectacular appearance. The nebula is visible to the unaided eye as a misty patch around the central star of the line of three that form Orion's sword.

Pomegranate, Box 6099, Rohnert Park, CA 94927

A VIEW OF THE UNIVERSE

NGC 6357, AN OBSCURED NEBULA IN THE PLANE OF THE
MILKY WAY

Most star-forming nebulae have a deep red color modified by
blue light, creating varying shades of magenta. NGC 6357,
however, shows no evidence of a blue component, nor any
sign of the bright blue stars normally found in these objects,
because fine dust through which we see the nebula selectively
removes blue light.

Pomegranate, Box 6099, Rohnert Park, CA 94927

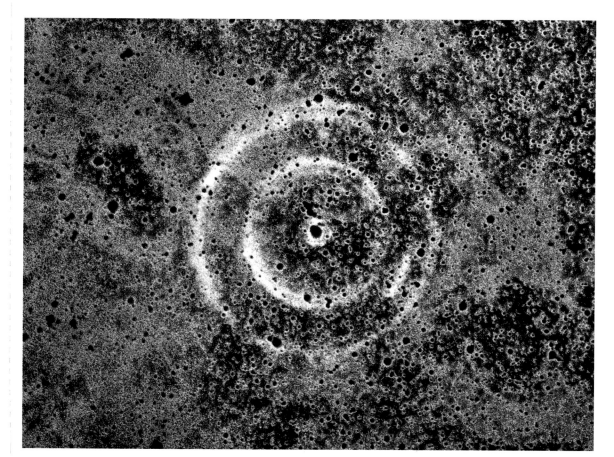

A VIEW OF THE UNIVERSE

THE TWIN LIGHT ECHOES OF SUPERNOVA 1987A

When supernova 1987A exploded in the Large Magellanic Cloud, the Milky Way's nearest companion galaxy, the brilliant flash of light took about 170,000 years to reach us. The dust responsible for the rings seen here lies in two distinct layers, about 470 and 1,300 light years from the supernova.

Pomegranate, Box 6099, Rohnert Park, CA 94927

A VIEW OF THE UNIVERSE

MESSIER 100 AND ITS DWARF COMPANIONS

Messier 100, the brightest spiral galaxy in the Virgo cluster of galaxies, about 60 million light years away, is shown in a photograph specially made to reveal the faint dwarf galaxies surrounding it. The dwarf galaxy at the top of the picture, NGC 4322, is close enough to interact with M100's large spiral and slightly distort its outer arms.

Pomegranate, Box 6099, Rohnert Park, CA 94927

A VIEW OF THE UNIVERSE

THE TARANTULA NEBULA AROUND 30 DORADUS
This object is the only extragalactic star-forming nebula that
can be seen with the unaided eye. A small telescope reveals
spindly tendrils of glowing gas, which have been likened to the
legs of a spider. The "body" of the spider is the bright nebula
seen at the center of the photograph.

Pomegranate, Box 6099, Rohnert Park, CA 94927

A VIEW OF THE UNIVERSE

REFLECTION NEBULA AROUND THE TRIFID NEBULA, M20
The spectacular Trifid Nebula (Messier 20) is a striking mixture
of brilliant red light emitted from excited hydrogen gas and the
soft blue glow of a reflection nebula. The dust lanes seem to
divide the nebula into three parts, hence the name "trifid,"
meaning cut into three.

Pomegranate, Box 6099, Rohnert Park, CA 94927